IF Not FOR THE Cat

IF Not FOR THE Cat

HAIKU BY
Jack Prelutsky

PAINTINGS BY
Ted Rand

SCHOLASTIC INC.
New York Toronto London Auckland Sydney
Mexico City New Delhi Hong Kong Buenos Aires

ISBN 0-439-79908-2

Text copyright © 2004 by Jack Prelutsky. Illustrations copyright © 2004 by Ted Rand.
All rights reserved. Published by Scholastic Inc., 557 Broadway, New York, NY 10012,
by arrangement with Greenwillow Books, an imprint of HarperCollins Publishers.
SCHOLASTIC and associated logos are trademarks and/or registered trademarks of Scholastic Inc.

12 11 10 9 8 7 6 5 4 3 2   5 6 7 8 9 10/0

Printed in the U.S.A.   40

First Scholastic printing, September 2005

The art is a mix of sumi brush drawings in India ink, traditional watercolors, chalk, spatter, and printmaking techniques.
It was done on rag stock watercolor paper and rice paper.

The text type is 32-point OPTIElizabeth.

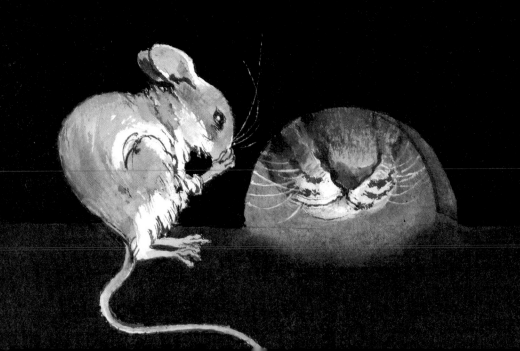

If not for the cat,
And the scarcity of cheese,
I could be content.

I, the hoverer,
Sip the nasturtium's nectar
And sing with my wings.

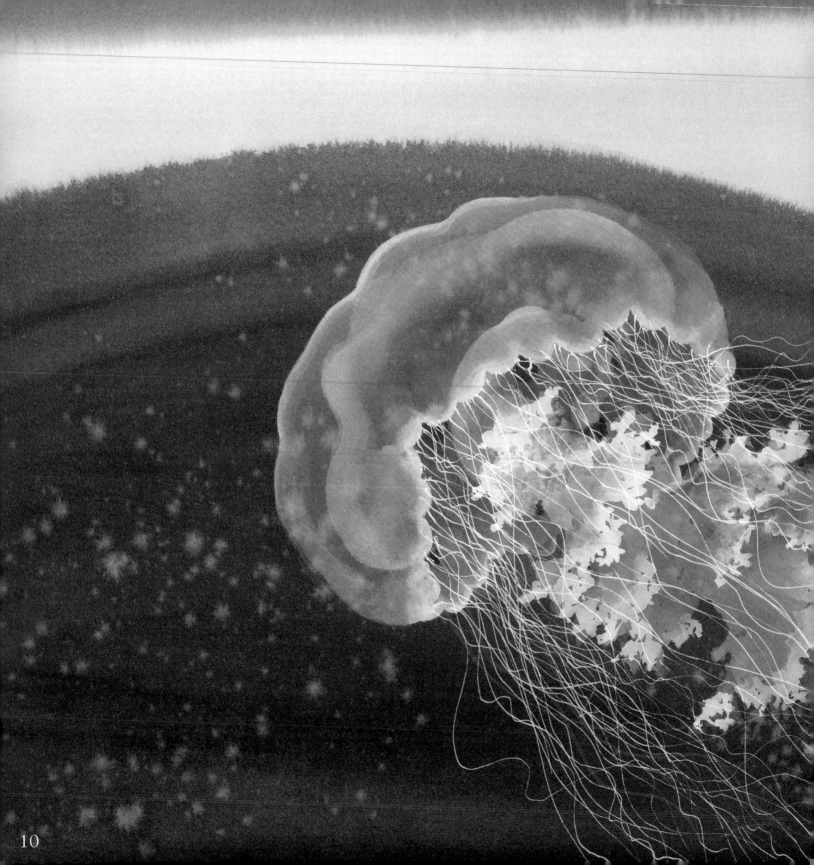

Boneless, translucent,
We undulate, undulate,
Gelatinously.

I am slow I am.
Slowest of the slow I am.
In my tree I am.

We are wrinkled hulks
With astonishing noses.
Our ears block the sun.

How foolish I am.
Why am I drawn to the flame
Which extinguishes?

Raucously we caw.
Your straw men do not fool us.
We burgle your corn.

I snack on my back,
Crack my dinner on my chest—
Bliss in the water.

Don't think about it—
Just leave the vicinity
If you hear my tail.

Gaudily feathered,
With nothing at all to say,
I can't stop talking.

We are we are we
Are we are we are we are
Many in our hill.

I spend all my time
Picking ants up with my tongue.
It's a busy life.

Safe inside my pouch
Sleeps the future of my kind—
Delicate and frail.

I have no hatchet
And yet I fell a forest.
My teeth are my tools.

From nests in the clouds
We survey our dominion
With telescope eyes.

When I raise my tail,
Expressing my displeasure,
Even wolves make tracks.

Wingless we went in,
But we emerged as fliers—
And oh, such colors!

Who is Who

Pages 6–7
A mouse

Pages 18–19
Crows

Pages 30–31
A kangaroo

Pages 8–9
A hummingbird

Pages 20–21
An otter

Pages 32–33
A beaver

Pages 10–11
Jellyfish (sea jellies)

Pages 22–23
A rattlesnake

Pages 34–35
Bald eagles

Pages 12–13
A sloth

Pages 24–25
A parrot

Pages 36–37
A skunk

Pages 14–15
Elephants

Pages 26–27
Ants

Pages 38–39
Butterflies

Pages 16–17
A moth

Pages 28–29
An anteater

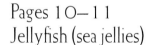
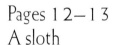